COPING WITH PAIN

SUE RIGBY

COPING WITH PAIN

ISBN 978-1-9998988-9-2

COPYRIGHT © 2021 SUE RIGBY

https://handsforhealing.net

With love to my family and with gratitude to Robert, who set me on the path to writing this book.

About Sue Rigby

Sue Rigby is a certified Quantum-Touch™ practitioner and instructor, and Reiki Master, teacher and practitioner.

She has an established practice in Shropshire, working with clients and students from all over the world. Her work is with both people and animals and combined with her own life experiences, has given her an insight into pain, both cause and effect.

Introduction

We are all familiar with pain.

It is part of our lives in one form or another. What is important is how we deal with it.

In these changing, global times, it is vital that we aware of ourselves and the way that we relate to the world around us. We can choose to make changes in the way we live and conduct ourselves, in order to keep ourselves healthy.

I have written this book with the aim of providing the reader with information and strategies to discover more about the causes of pain and alternative ways of dealing with it.

How should I describe pain?

Pain has many facets and is multi-layered. It can be physical, mental, emotional, and spiritual.

It can be life-changing, all-consuming, and all-encompassing. It can take over, destroying your life as you know it.

Alongside the practical day-to-day changes, pain can change you and affect your loved ones. You may become irritable and withdrawn. You may not wish to interact with others. It can fill your whole being, consuming you with feelings of desperation, as you wonder when and if it will end.

Is it sharp or dull? Is it intermittent or constant?

You can wake up feeling fine for a few moments and then, WHAM, it resurfaces.

You can feel immense loneliness.

We only know what our own pain feels like. No-one can know what it's like to walk in another's shoes; we can only imagine.

We only see the face people present to the world.

A look at pain

This book is intended for those who are trying to understand their pain and the help that is available. I hope that everyone, including healers, medical professionals, or people in pain, can take something from this book. We all look at life differently, taking different stances. Some of us will only use traditional Western medicine, while some look for other ways to find help and ease. One of my aims with this book is to provide a starting point for those who are looking at alternative ways to deal with pain. There are many therapies available and you will find details of some at the end of the book.

We all experience pain at some time in our lives. I have experienced physical pain with illness and injuries. I have a deformed pelvis and, following surgery as a young child, I spent five months in hospital, much of it encased in plaster. I also contracted whooping cough during this time and can recall being in isolation. As the years went by, I developed arthritis in my hip and was in great pain as I waited for a replacement. Quantum-Touch™ was a great help to me when problems flared up.

I experienced emotional pain due to the trauma of separation from my family when I was in hospital as a child. I have experienced emotional pain with the loss of loved ones. My first major loss was my father. At the age of eighteen, I was living and working abroad and was unable to return home before his funeral. His wish was that I stay and make the most of my opportunities. This has caused considerable trauma and mental pain. I have since lost many loved ones, including three siblings. I had great difficulty coping with the loss of my eldest brother, as I had been unable to grieve properly following the death of my father.

Mental pain has also featured in my life. I worked in banking and became stressed and depressed when my portfolio of customers increased massively overnight, and I was unable to cope and complete my work to the standards I had set myself. I am usually quite a positive, optimistic, strong person, and see my glass as half-full, but was unable to apply that viewpoint to the circumstances I found myself in. I was unable to work for ten years but I eventually found my way out of this situation.

I was helped through this by loved ones and came to realise that the Reiki I been attuned to some years earlier offered me a way to move forward. With the support of a friend, I set up my business offering Reiki treatments and found great satisfaction and purpose in this.

As I practised more and more Reiki, I had Reiki Share sessions with a friend. In one of our chats, she told me about Quantum-Touch™ and asked me if I had come across it. At that time, I hadn't and I was quite content to just offer Reiki sessions to clients. However, when I went home and investigated Quantum-Touch™, I was hooked and booked a place on my first workshop immediately, taking my first steps on a continuing journey.

When I discovered Quantum-Touch™, I hoped that it was a way that I could help myself.

At that time, I was experiencing pain in my hip. I received a steroid injection and that was effective for about six weeks. I was in constant pain, taking painkillers as often as I could, limping and leaning to one side as I walked, and having trouble sleeping because of the pain.

4

The potential I could see in Quantum-Touch™ excited me and as I made my way to my first workshop, I was anticipating positive changes. During the first morning, as we discovered the techniques and practised them, my hips realigned and my posture straightened. As the workshop continued over the course of two days, my pain reduced significantly. I had no need for painkillers. Over the following week, I gave myself daily sessions and the pain didn't return.

I attended more workshops, becoming a practitioner. As I saw more evidence of the impact that Quantum-Touch™ can have, I progressed further and became an instructor.

I regularly see amazing improvements in my clients and my expectations have changed. In Quantum-Touch™ we refer to these as 'normacles'. I look forward with joy to every Quantum-Touch™ session, never knowing what to expect.

I have seen clients achieve profound and long-lasting changes for the better. Some no longer need surgery; some are pain-free; some find peace of mind, and some find Quantum-Touch gives them a coping mechanism. All of these changes are due to the work of their own inner healer and so each Quantum-Touch™ experience is unique.

Often, when we despair of obtaining the help that we need from medical professionals, we begin to widen our search and make startling discoveries. We find new paths and new ways of being. Our lives and outlook can change.

For most of us, our first step is to visit our GP and follow the traditional route. We may have been prescribed treatment and this may or may not have helped. If we have found that there has been no improvement, we might visit our GP again. This time, our medication may be changed. We may have gone through this process a number of times, trying to find medication that suits us and which alleviates or resolves the problem. We may find that we experience adverse side effects from medication and exhaust the available medicines, o choose not to take them because of the side effects and long term impacts.

When the GP has exhausted the initial method of treatments we may then be referred for investigations. These can involve X-rays, scans and blood tests, with a subsequent referral to a consultant. This can mean more investigations, some of which can be invasive. All of this is very time-consuming. Our GP clinics and hospitals are working under great pressure and there can be a long wait for appointments. Often, months can pass without any respite.

Sometimes, a person may be told that nothing is wrong, but this is not what their body is telling them. Frustration begins to surface and they may look for alternative ways to find ease

Every pain, disease or illness is a communication from our body. Pain is a message that we must attend to.

We might ask for a second opinion.

When I did this, I found that I was referred back to the same department and I therefore asked for a second opinion at a different hospital, with a general consultant.

When nothing changed, I visited my GP again and frustratingly I was referred back to the original department. This time, I was listened to and was referred to a different specialism at another hospital trust. Here, I found that I would have to wait at least nine months to see the consultant and I made the decision to ask for a private appointment.

As I had been unable to take previously prescribed medication because of food intolerances, and I was unwilling to take some of them because of adverse effects, I was fortunate to find my consultant was a forward-looking doctor. He was willing to listen and think outside traditional parameters, and was actively involved in research for alternative therapies.

I was prescribed gut-focused hypnotherapy and medication. My medication was the only one available to me because of my food intolerances. I am no longer taking this medication. I give myself regular Quantum-Touch™ sessions and receive them from friends, along with trying alternative therapies.

Some people are very open to trying different ways to help themselves, especially when they have exhausted traditional means of treatment. There are so many alternatives available and it is a matter of investigating them and finding one that seems right for you, doing your own research, and looking for recommendations from others you know well.

As a Certified Practitioner and Level 1 and 2 Instructor, I have great faith in Quantum-Touch®. There are many alternatives: acupuncture, osteopathy, chiropractic, physiotherapy, gym, Pilates, Reiki, yoga, hypnosis, healers, psychotherapy, counselling, sound healing, herbalists. This only scratches the surface.

You can consult psychics, clairvoyants, mediums, or spiritual healers. You can turn to your religious beliefs and gain strength there.

You can ask for a referral to a pain clinic, where you may be given advice on coping with pain, including trying meditation. The benefits of meditation can be profound, working on many different levels.

The effects of pain on our lives can be measured in many ways other than physical. You may find your normal activities curtailed and be unable to work. The implications of this are not just financial but social, mental and emotional too, impacting your health in other ways. You may find that you have to negotiate your way through the benefits system at a time when you are badly placed to do so. You may need carers and other support.

It can be a time when you find out who your true friends really are and who will stick with you through thick and thin.

You are faced with choices you never anticipated and decisions you don't want to make.

Pain has a new relevance for so many people following the arrival of Covid-19 across the world. Death, severe illness, long-lasting symptoms, fear, isolation, separation, grief, redundancies, closure of businesses and trauma have become daily watchwords on the television and in the newspapers.

I am fortunate that I have remained in general good health and I am very grateful for this.

So, What Do You Do?

Do you just get on with it or do you give up? Do you hide away from life and all its unexpected joys? Do you succumb to depression?

Do you look for other ways?

Sometimes, a realisation can just hit you and help you change your mindset and other times you can find yourself on a long, slow and painful journey.

Just as pain changes us, we need to change ourselves to find our way through.

The simplest thing to do is smile and fake it until you make it. We can make a choice and be agents of change, shining a light for ourselves and others.

Others suffer with us when we are in pain and by being the best we can be, we can alleviate their suffering a little too.

But for a variety of reasons, not everybody is able to do this.

Pain Journey

Where do you start and where does it end?

Pain is a sign that something is wrong on some level. Your body is sending you a signal and asking you to take action. Physical pain does not necessarily signify a physical cause.

Causes can be physical, mental, emotional or spiritual.

They can be related to past events impacting you or those close to you.

They can be events that you have forgotten or blocked from your mind.

They can be events that you believe you have dealt with successfully but more emotional work needs to be done to release emotions linked to past traumas.

Working as a Quantum-Touch® practitioner and instructor, I see many amazing changes. Often, a physical problem has an emotional cause which shows itself in many guises, finding a weakness in a body and using that weakness to communicate.

Pain is subjective and personal.

What is extremely painful to one person may be less so to another. We are often asked to rate pain on a scale of 0 to 10, with 10 being the most painful and 0 being total comfort and ease. For those who find it difficult to rate pain, there is the Lego Pain Face Scale, with illustrations to help show the level of pain. You can find examples of the images on the internet.

Symptoms can be many and varied, including digestive issues, nerve pain, structural and spinal problems, stress and depression. You may develop a serious condition such as cancer. Some conditions seem to be becoming increasingly common. Cancer now affects one in two people. Whether this is down to our lifestyle, environment, other issues, an ageing population, or a combination of causes is a question for scientists to answer. No matter the level of severity of the condition, the impact on an individual is powerful, causing much distress.

You may be able to help yourself through simple measures such as changing your diet and taking up exercise. This can be empowering and good for your long-term health. You may, however, undergo more serious treatments such as surgery and chemotherapy.

Causes of Pain

There are many possible causes of pain. Often there is more than one cause, and more than one effect.

Addiction

This takes many forms, from alcohol to drugs, whether illegal or prescribed. The mental and emotional toll caused by addiction is immense, not just to the addict but to those around them. It takes great courage to face up to an addiction, hard work to break the habit, and a lifetime to maintain balance. Just as the addict struggles to cope, so do their families. Addiction can lead to family breakdown, mental illness, poor health, marriage failures, job loss, crime, criminal convictions, prison sentences, and homelessness. Even when the habit is broken, the temptations are always there, always calling.

Bullying, Harassment and Discrimination

There have always been bullies who have inflicted physical and emotional pain. Bullying can take place anywhere; in schools, among so-called friends, and in workplaces. It can be direct or subtle. Children demand lunches, possessions and money from others, using the threat of violence and exclusion. People in positions of power demean and ridicule employees in front of colleagues, they harass their colleagues and sexual and racial discrimination are still major issues.

In our modern technological society, bullies have new ways to cause harm. The growth of cyber bullying and trolling is continuing unchecked, with major companies failing to halt this. Online accounts are set up in false names, leaving the recipient of messages unable to identify the sender.

People in the public eye are easy targets. Society has changed. It seems to have become acceptable for people to express harmful, adverse opinions and judgements of others and to make threats. It seems that those who are 'different' – those who stand out and those who dare to stand up for what they believe is right – can become targets for the bullies.

Children are picked on for being overweight, timid, clever, wearing glasses, for being loners, for any kind of perceived difference.

The impacts of bullying are profound and can last a lifetime. Some choose to commit suicide as they believe that is the only way to escape the trauma they are facing.

Chemicals

We are still unaware of the dangers of many of the chemicals that we use on a daily basis. Matters become more confused when one government or official body sanctions the use of certain chemicals and another bans them.

When we stop and take a look at the number of chemicals that we use each day, it is astounding. They are in our toiletries, our cleaning products, and processed foods. In our foods, they are often disguised as very long, scientific-sounding names, as companies moved away from calling them E numbers. I came across one in processed food that acts as a starch to bind the ingredients together and at the same time is a laxative!

We use them in our gardens and our cars. They are in our soft furnishings and furniture and they permeate the air we breathe. Plastic containers contain many chemicals, which break down slowly.

Ultimately, many find their way into the environment, the earth, our watercourses and oceans, and eventually into our food.

Our bodies did not evolve to ingest these chemicals and our natural world is struggling to cope with their impact. More and more people are becoming sensitive to the chemicals in their everyday surroundings and developing severe allergies.

Diet

Our world is changing and the foods that we eat have changed dramatically over the past fifty years. We eat food that is processed, stored in plastics, and harvested before maturity in order to travel vast distances to the destination of sale; foods that have been treated with chemicals, and foods whose constituents differ from those our digestive systems evolved to cope with. Some of our foods may be months old before we eat them. It stands to reason that our bodies face an onslaught and are sometimes are unable to cope.

The symptoms that we have are not solely related to digestive issues. We may experience a wide variety of illnesses that could ultimately be resolved by a change in diet.

Pain that we experience may be caused by intolerances to certain foods or constituents of those foods. Whatever the causes, many people find themselves experiencing pain and have to adjust their diet to cope in an effort to find relief.

People suffering with Irritable Bowel Syndrome (IBS) may

choose to adopt a diet of foods low in FODMAPs (Fermentable Oligosaccharides, Disaccharides, Monosaccharides and Polyols) in an effort to avoid the pain and bloating which are common symptoms of IBS.

Maybe we as a nation should be looking at changing the way we produce our foods.

Those suffering with arthritic-type pain may choose to eliminate foods from the nightshade family (white potatoes, aubergine, tomatoes, bell peppers, cayenne pepper and paprika).

In an effort to deal with other problems, some choose to adopt paleo or keto diets. Advocates of these diets suggest that by eating low carbohydrate, low fat foods, inflammation in the body can be reduced, bringing benefits such as weight loss and the improvements in conditions such as Type 2 diabetes and auto-immune conditions, including Alzheimer's Disease, Parkinson's Disease and Multiple Sclerosis. It is also suggested that other health problems such as migraines, strokes and digestive issues may be affected positively. There are many websites offering information and you may find it helpful to investigate further. Basic information can be found at: https://www.nhs.uk/live-well/healthy-weight/top-diets-review/

Vitamin deficiency diseases are still present in current times, whether caused by poor diet, poverty, or physical problems which prevent the absorption of nutrients. Sometimes a person's ethnicity or where they live can influence their ability to process nutrients. In the UK, we suffer from a lack of sunlight from October to March, leading to some people experiencing Vitamin D deficiency.

Whatever choices we make, it is important to do thorough research to ensure we are obtaining all the nutrients that we need. Every day, there are articles in the press stating that a certain food is good for alleviating a certain condition, only for the following day another article to be published disputing these claims. We must ensure that we are not following trends that benefit vested interests, making sure that we research and take advice to find those that are of benefit.

Disease

We may be outwardly healthy yet still succumb to disease.

Sometimes, we are not even aware that we have had a disease for some time, until symptoms surface and are investigated. We have all heard of people who have developed cancer and not known until vague symptoms are investigated at too late a stage. Sadly, there are people who carry on regardless, thinking that they are suffering from something trivial, and don't bother to visit a doctor. Alternatively, there are those who have severe problems who are too scared to see a doctor. When they finally do, they find that they have left it too late.

Early trauma

Taking an alternative viewpoint, some medical professionals are coming to believe that traumatic events in our early years have an impact upon us in later years. Early 20th century French psychologist and psychotherapist Pierre Janet took this viewpoint. Few of us can remember events in our lives before the age of three but physical, mental and emotional trauma can become rooted in our body, only later showing itself in different ways. This is the basis for the ideology of Quantum-Touch™ Self Created Health.

Taking this a step further, there are some who believe that a person has past lives that impact on this life. Some choose to undergo past-life regression to find relief and answers. This may release trauma. It should only be undertaken by highly experienced and highly recommended professionals and practitioners, to help deal with any aftermath and offer continuing support.

This takes us further, to look at the idea of Karma. Do we choose the life we wish to be born to, and actions in this life? Do past lives and ancestors' lives have impact and repercussions? This raises questions and ideas such as:

If you are suffering pain, are you repaying a debt?

What action can you take to transmute this?

Where can you go for help with this?

Should you try hypnotherapy?

Do you seek guidance from psychics and mediums?

What can you do to positively influence and change your life?

I have met people who have changed their lives for the better by taking a path such as those mentioned above. It is possible to change your life completely with support from trusted practitioners.

Emotional and mental pain

Not all pain is physical, yet emotional problems can show themselves in physical and mental problems, just as physical problems can produce emotional and mental pain. They are linked and very real.

We can experience emotional pain in widely varying circumstances. Grief over the death of a loved one; going through a separation; as a victim of bullying; struggling to conceive. There are just a few examples.

Judgements by others causes pain, too. Sometimes we can cause pain unknowingly in social situations. You will probably have heard of people who have been asked why they haven't started a family, yet they may have experienced miscarriages or been unable to conceive, and have no wish to discuss deeply private matters.

We impose our own world views and opinions without thinking of the implications for others. With the growth of reality TV and celebrity culture, we have begun to feel entitled to judge others.

Words spoken to us can have lasting impacts which emerge years later. We may be told that we are overweight, can't sing, or are untidy, and take this to heart. Being mocked has the same effect. We may feel shame or embarrassment.

In these situations, we try our best to cope and work our way through them. We may forget them over the years. We may even feel that we have resolved the issues. However, at a later date, we can experience physical pain and it is a way for our bodies to tell us that we still have work to do to make ourselves whole again.

Mental pain is a special concern during the Covid-19 pandemic. Lockdowns, shielding and self-isolation are causing an exponential increase in mental health problems. Isolation and fear severely impact mental health. The whole population of the UK has been impacted.

On the positive side, we have seen wonderful examples of community spirit, people have found new activities to occupy themselves and digital communication has proved to be a lifeline for many, from the youngest to the oldest. We have learned new digital skills and found time to appreciate the beauty of nature.

This has not been the case for everyone. Some have found themselves working on the frontline and have been fearful for their own safety and that of loved ones. Some have had to live away from family members in order to keep them safe. Some have seen their colleagues and loved ones contract Covid-19 and die. No hospital visiting has been allowed. Goodbyes have been given over the telephone or video call and funerals have changed. The correct Personal Protective Equipment has been unavailable or in short supply. Supermarkets have struggled to cope with the surge in demand for essentials. Employees have worked from home, been furloughed, or made redundant. Some businesses have thrived while others have closed for good or are struggling.

Underneath all this, fear and loneliness have increased until people are in pain. We have to find a way through this. The support of others can be heartening, giving a safety net and providing a lifeline.

The way we behave can have a major impact on others. If we are in pain, we may become irritable and withdraw from our loved ones, failing to communicate our problems and unknowingly causing them pain in turn. They may not understand what we are going through, as we may have felt unable to tell them. We may not even understand what our problem is. We can damage relationships unintentionally just by withdrawing inwards.

In extreme cases, problems may take the form of physical and mental abuse. Drug abuse by family members causes immense pain and fear to loved ones, who can struggle to cope with the changes they see in the person and their behaviours. It places an immense strain on families and causes untold harm as they try to hold things together, never knowing what to expect from one day to the next.

Environment and climate

This links in closely with chemicals. Our crops are sprayed many times over before they reach our tables. The chemicals are leaching into our soil and harming wildlife, leaking into our watercourses, and therefore our water supply. Our everyday use of plastics is increasing, working their way into the food chain. Chemicals are making their way into food and drink with effects that are not fully known. We did not evolve to digest plastics. They are everywhere and we do not dispose of them properly. We see massive islands of plastic in our oceans and hear of animals harmed as they become entangled in plastics or eat them in their search for food.

Chemicals such as fluoride can be added to our water. What are the effects of that on our bodies? Should fluoride be added to the water supply without our permission? In effect, it is the mass medication of the population without their consent.

As our environment changes, so do the creatures and organisms within it. Some have previously been seen in other countries and have migrated as climate changes. Unfamiliar ticks and bugs and different health hazards present themselves.

Functional and System Failure

Sometimes our bodies develop a fault, just like machinery can. Our bodies are very complex and need rest, exercise and maintenance to thrive. By eating healthily and following guidelines, we give ourselves the best chances to stay healthy but nevertheless this approach doesn't always work. In these cases, medication and/or surgery are often needed. This may bring about a full return to health but at other times only a partial return to health is achieved. It can be the start of a journey of differing pains.

Injuries

These are a common cause of pain and vary hugely in severity. We know that even a small paper cut is painful. Some injuries we can recover from quickly, while others cause damage that is permanent and life-changing. Some can involve a long period of recovery and rehabilitation and leave us in pain. The emotional impact of the injury is as damaging as the physical aspect. The injury affects not just the injured party but loved ones too.

Large, multi-national corporations

You may question the inclusion of this category. I believe that large corporations, pharmaceutical companies and oil companies have huge vested interests in ensuring that we continue to purchase their goods. They are not looking for more natural, alternative ways to prosper, and they answer only to their shareholders. As a world, we must wake up to the harm to ourselves and the world in general that we are allowing them to perpetuate. They have the ears of politicians and governments and bring prosperity to economies. At what cost to us?

Medication and Vaccinations

We commonly take the drugs that medical practitioners prescribe. The list of side effects of many are alarming, causing different problems and pains. It is common to hear of people who take one drug to counter the effects of another and then another to counter the effects of the second drug. As we age and our bodies deteriorate, we can see this more frequently, with older people often taking a cocktail of drugs.

Pharmaceutical companies are very powerful. They use aggressive forms of marketing and their representatives are frequent visitors to medical practices. We see the same drug marketed and packaged in different ways for over-the-counter purchase, supposedly for different symptoms. It's always good to ask a pharmacist for advice before buying.

Some medications are vital to our survival but others not so much. It is our responsibility to look in detail at any medication we are prescribed, to check its ingredients, purpose and side effects in consultation with medical professionals, and to decide whether we are happy to take it. Our doctors should be happy to discuss alternatives with us.

We also take supplements and over-the-counter products and we must be aware of any interactions and reactions. There is a rise in the number of people buying medications online in an attempt to help themselves. This sometimes has an adverse impact.

We need to be aware of the growing resistance of bacteria to antibiotics, and the dangers facing us as a result of this. We should take antibiotics responsibly, ensuring that we complete the whole course as prescribed.

Vaccinations against viral infections raise an entirely different series of questions and we all make our own judgements about their suitability. The effects of these judgements have seen a rise in the number of measles cases, as more parents choose not to have their children immunised based on the information available to them at the relevant times. It is very hard to distinguish between genuine sources of information and fake news, and to know what and who to trust.

This is a very controversial area and will continue to be so. Many people are healthy because of vaccinations and the protection they have delivered. We may never know how many cases of serious disease have been prevented by vaccinations.

As more people question reported side-effects of vaccinations and the power of pharmaceutical companies, this trend may continue.

With the current coronavirus pandemic (November 2019) and the rush by scientists worldwide to devise a vaccine to protect against this virus, just a few of the many questions that come to my mind are "How safe will any vaccine be?", "How will they be tested to determine long-term side effects on humans?", 'For how long will they be tested before it is decided that they are safe?", "Will the vaccines be rushed out too early?", and 'Are the pharmaceutical companies, governments or scientists holding the power in these decisions?"

Also - "How many Governments will sign a 'No Blame' deal with the pharmaceutical companies?", thus freeing the pharmaceutical companies from any liability in the event of adverse impacts.

There are many different points of view regarding this. Questions are asked as to whether the vaccines, the pharmaceutical companies, international organisations such as the World Health Organisation, United Nations, the Bill and Melinda Gates Foundation, and even national governments can be trusted. Many feel that business interests are being placed ahead of individuals and their welfare. Others point to these suggestions as conspiracy theories.

The enforced lockdown, isolation and shielding have meant that we have found new ways to occupy our time and rediscovered old ways that bring us pleasure. It has led to a huge increase in the use of social media and an increase in the amount of information placed there for all to see. We have also seen many ideas and suggestions that are viewed as weird and wonderful, and many others offering cheap, practical solutions by medical professionals have been dismissed. Could this be because the pharmaceutical companies would not make massive profits? As YouTube videos have proliferated during the Covid-19 pandemic, many have been removed by YouTube on the basis of being conspiracy theories. Who influences social media and who has the right to decide that something is a conspiracy theory? Could it be those that benefit the most if they are allowed to go ahead with their plans unhindered? How much trust should we place in our governments and scientists and is it democratic to remove an item because some say it is inaccurate? We don't know who is correct but to remove an item because some disagree with it takes away freedom of speech and could be seen as an abuse of power.

We would be placing ourselves in the hands of scientists, researchers and pharmaceutical companies, who will be relishing the power and income that this crisis provides. We would be putting a great deal of trust in them.

As the vaccination programme is being successfully rolled out in the UK, many elderly and vulnerable people have already received their first vaccination (February 2021), and are looking forward to the promise of lockdowns ending regaining lost freedom, meeting friends and resuming normal activity whilst having the protection of the vaccine.

We must all make up our own minds, allowing and respecting the views of others without judgement.

If you experience an adverse reaction to a medication, you should refer to a medical professional for advice. Following this, in the UK they should report this side effect using the Yellow Card Reporting System. Individuals can also use this system. For more information see:

https://yellowcard.mhra.gov.uk/

Post-Traumatic Stress Disorder (PTSD)

We live in stressful times and the stress we deal with in the modern world differs from that experienced in earlier times. When the 'fight or flight' mechanism evolved, it was to enable us to flee from sabre-toothed tigers, or stand and defend ourselves. The causes of our stresses now differ but the response remains the same.

PTSD is usually experienced shortly after a major trauma in our lives, commonly within about one month, and can last for years. It can, however, take longer to develop, sometimes months or years. Experienced, professional, medical help is the first step, followed by other therapies recommended to you by professionals, such as Cognitive Behavioural Therapy (CBT).

It is forecast that there will be a large number of cases of PTSD following the Covid-19 pandemic. Hospital workers, care workers and other key workers have been placed in traumatic situations and had to deal with these on a daily basis for a sustained period of time. As we arrive at a new 'normal' and the hope of improvement is on the horizon, these traumas will begin to surface. Help and support are vital.

Being kind to yourself is important and this is where complementary and alternative therapies may be important for someone experiencing PTSD.

Radiation and emissions

We are impacted constantly by radiation all around us. Rapid advances in technology are changing our home- and working-environments and their impacts are not fully known or even investigated. The roll-out of 5G technology is being hailed as a considerable advance in some quarters and an area of untold damage to humans and wildlife in others.

Receiving an adverse prognosis

Sometimes physicians have to deliver devastating news to patients. How should we react? Just receiving the news of a terminal diagnosis is an incredibly painful experience. It may prompt us to sort out our affairs, and that is no bad thing in itself. Why should we rely on a prognosis? If we accept what we are told, do we just wait for the inevitable, or do we forge our own path to a more positive prognosis? We may know of friends and loved ones who go into remission from cancer with no explanation. We can have a positive impact on our lives and futures, changing the seemingly unchangeable.

If it is not possible to change that future, a positive attitude may bring ways of adjusting to it and coping with the outcome, which benefits both you and your loved ones.

Stress

As we evolved, we developed the 'fight or flight' mechanism to enable survival. In stressful situations, our bodies will produce adrenaline to give us a rapid burst of energy, allowing us to do just that. In the intensive world in which we live today, many people continually have high levels of adrenaline in their systems.

One little-discussed aspect of this mechanism is the choice to 'freeze'. In nature documentaries we see animals who freeze to protect themselves from predators. We are no different and we can become frozen in a state of fear.

Each individual can cope with different levels of stress and responds differently to stress.

What stresses one person may not stress another. Some of us thrive on stress, living fast-paced lives that others would find stressful, and can continue to do this for many years. Some cope with this lifestyle for a period of time before experiencing burnout. Others know themselves and choose a slower pace of life, living within their limits.

I have frequently seen people who set high standards for themselves become stressed when they are unable to meet those standards, which can lead to stress and depression.

Stress is a very personal experience and can be hard to communicate effectively. Some life events are known to be particularly stressful; for example, bereavement and divorce. Holmes and Rahe developed a scale in 1967 which allocated points to various events, giving higher points to the most stressful events. When these are added up, the total gives an indicator of whether a person is likely to be stressed.

This was followed by the Perceived Stress Scale (PSS), which was devised in 1983. It asks questions about a person's feelings and thoughts over the preceding month and the answers lead to a score, rating levels of stress.

The above are just tools to make an initial assessment, before deciding on the course of action appropriate to the individual.

It is very easy to plough on, doing our impression of Superman or Superwoman, thinking that we can cope, and denying that we have a problem. When we do eventually admit to ourselves that we have a problem, it is often at quite an advanced stage and may take longer to resolve.

When we become aware of our own levels of stress, we can take steps to minimise the problems. We may have to make tough decisions, such as changing job; perhaps choosing to receive lower pay but ultimately protecting our mental, physical and emotional health.

Once someone has experienced stress, they become more aware of their own signs of this, which can prompt them to perform activities that they personally find relieve those symptoms. Some find that simply stepping back from commitments: taking a walk; meditating; having a relaxing bath; booking an appointment with an alternative therapist, and taking time to nurture themselves, are ideal first steps.

It is common for someone who is feeling stressed to experience general ill health. Our immune systems govern our response to stress. Whenever we experience a period of stress and find ourselves in constant fight or flight mode, our immune systems direct their primary response to that and change focus away from protecting our bodies from infections. We then find ourselves weakened and more vulnerable to ill-health.

Beliefs

As I have worked more and more deeply with Quantum-Touch® and Reiki, I have discovered that I am developing spiritually and psychically, becoming more aware on many different levels. I have begun to work with spirit as I give a healing session. This is an ongoing process and is changing my viewpoint.

Quantum-Touch® has strengthened my belief that anything is possible. When you receive a 'healing' it is not the 'healer' who is healing you. You are 'healing' yourself. Your body has an innate intelligence and knows what the problem is. It has a wonderful ability to heal itself but when you are ill or in pain it lacks the energy to do so effectively. When you receive a healing, your body takes over, doing what it can to help itself. Your beliefs about what is or is not possible do not change the possibilities but I have found that a person's intention to allow any healing to take place does have an impact. Some people feel little at the time of a healing and then discover changes manifesting themselves over a period of time.

If you have been repeatedly told that recovery is not possible, you may have accepted that idea. You may have resigned yourself to your situation and aligned yourself with the 'new you'. You may have accepted the new identity forced upon you and your life. You may be living on benefits and fear any improvements in your health will mean that you lose your benefits.

How will you survive? Can you resume your work and maintain your standard of living? You may have become the person that people associate with a certain condition and feel sorry for identifying you with the condition instead of seeing the real you.

Who would you become if you allowed yourself to heal?

Alternatively, you may be the person who believes that anything is possible, without limits. You can overcome many things and change your life for the better, with determination and a 'mind over matter' attitude.

When you receive a 'healing', you will permit your body to do what it can to help itself, and see incredible changes. You will work hard to look for solutions, taking whatever action you can to move forward.

Quantum-Touch is an alternative therapy that aims to bring about a reduction in pain and spontaneous realignment of bones. A face-to-face 'healing' session usually involves the practitioner placing their hands on areas the client has indicated are causing problems. Often, the practitioner moves on to work on other areas as the session progresses. Depending upon the therapy, the client may experience sensations such as heat and cold, tingling or numbness, or changes in the levels of pain. This can sometimes increase before diminishing. A great sense of peace and relaxation may follow and a release of painful emotions. You will work with a range of people from medical professionals to complementary and alternative therapists to bring about change.

I have seen incredible changes in people. Changes that others may have believed to be impossible. In Quantum-Touch®, we have begun to call these 'normacles'.

I believe that it is within us all to change our lives. Our life path may have been set out for us but our actions have impact. Some people accept their path and others seek to change theirs. Ultimately, people can be helped within the limits of their choices. Sadly, some people have shorter lives and we see many loved ones die before their time. We cannot change that for them.

Belief in what may be possible is extremely powerful. The messages we give to the world and the universe are heard and responded to. By having positive beliefs, we can begin to help ourselves.

The Law of Attraction states that we attract to ourselves whatever our thoughts are transmitting to the universe. When our thoughts are positive, we attract positive events and outcomes to us and, conversely, when we have negative thoughts, we attract negative events and outcomes. The power of our thoughts and intentions has great strength. When we have a personal vibration of love and gratitude for the many great blessings in our lives, we can see changes for the better.

There are many books and workshops about the Law of attracting what we want in our lives. Quantum-Touch now offer a 'Manifesting Miracles' workshop. You may wish to read *Ask and It Is Given* by Esther and Jerry Hicks. A CD by Dr Noah St. John, *The Great Little Book Of Afformations*, is available, detailing how our thoughts can influence our lives.

Signpost to therapies

The information below only scratches the surface of the many complementary and alternative therapies that are available. Some are mainstream and others are not. These are not recommendations but some background information for you to use if you wish to explore and research different options.

Check that all therapists are registered and certified practitioners before you consult them. Do your research and ask for recommendations from people you respect. Word of mouth is the best recommendation you can get.

You may wish to try a combination of therapies, finding that one therapy will ease one aspect of your pain, whilst another will help in a different way. For example, some Quantum-Touch® practitioners may combine that with other therapies, such as Reiki, while some counsellors use a combination of counselling and EFT (Emotional Freedom Technique). You will find that you are drawn to a particular therapy and that it will feel right for you.

If you share your experiences with others, you will probably find that it differs from someone else having the same therapy. We are all unique and your experience will be unique to you.

These therapies may be highly effective in alleviating your problems in alternative, holistic ways, but may not be sufficient for some issues. When seeking alternative, holistic help, always be aware of your own condition and seek medical help if required, as some conditions can need urgent medical intervention. When your condition improves and you wish to adjust dosages of any medication, it is vital to always do so under medical supervision.

The contributors to this section are either fellow therapists, practitioners and psychics, or the professional associations of the relevant therapy. Some practice at Mystique – a psychic and wellbeing centre in Shrewsbury, UK – and also maintain their own separate practices. Others have practices elsewhere. Many are skilled in more than one therapy.

Some therapies can be given over distance and others have to be in person. Many practitioners have changed the ways in which they work during the coronavirus pandemic.

I will begin with an explanation of Quantum-Touch® and Reiki, as these are my own specialisms.

Quantum-Touch®

This is a hands-on or hands-off complementary energy healing therapy using Life Force Energy, which can be given in person or over distance, helping the body to enhance its own natural healing abilities.

The practitioner maintains a high level of energy using a variety of techniques, allowing the client, in effect, to become their own healer. Our bodies have an innate intelligence and know what the problem is. When we are ill, injured or in pain, our energy levels are depleted and our bodies are less effective at helping themselves to heal. This higher level of energy enables our bodies to begin to help heal themselves, re-energising even the smallest particles in our bodies.

The client can be standing, seated, or lying down.

Quantum-Touch® may bring rapid relief of pain, realignment of bones with the lightest touch, speedier recovery from injuries, deep relaxation, ease depression and anxiety, and bring emotional release. It may be used for an untold number of conditions. It may bring many benefits, often unexpected, as the body may prioritise a different area than imagined. Quantum-Touch® works on many levels – physical, mental, emotional and spiritual.

Some practitioners use a Quantum-Touch® Pendant to enhance the benefits further.

The number of treatments needed can vary, depending on a number of factors, such as how long you have had a condition. More details can be found at www.handsforhealing.net, www.youtube.com/channel/UCn8EvNOSmuTrPYz1oaOz6dQ, and the official website of Quantum-Touch®: www.quantumtouch.com.

Quantum-Touch®, Self-Created Health

This is an energy healing therapy, which aims to discover the root cause behind physical, mental and emotional problems. This has special relevance at the moment as an increase in other health problems is expected in the aftermath of the coronavirus pandemic.

There can be often an emotional cause behind physical health problems. This cause can relate to events many years ago that we believe we have dealt with effectively. We move on and continue our lives but eventually our bodies send us a message that something is wrong and needs to be dealt with.

Once the cause is discovered and the emotion linked to it, the client is then guided through a process, bringing about the release of the emotions and allowing them to move forward through insight, remorse, forgiveness and self-love. This in turn brings relief, which can be intense.

The process is simple, yet profound, needing the client's commitment to follow the short process in order to gain the maximum benefit.

You can find a highly skilled practitioner by visiting www.quantumtouch.com and searching under Self Created Health Instructors.

YouTube: https://youtu.be/d6DranKF770

Reiki

Reiki is a Japanese word. The word 'Rei' means 'universal wisdom' and 'Ki' is 'life energy'.

Using Life Force Energy, we work with the seven main Chakra and energy fields, allowing them to speed up their own healing. The body chooses where to direct the energy to achieve this. In this way, it can be used when you are experiencing pain and illness.

The client usually lies down for the session.

It is associated with deep relaxation, peace of mind, stress reduction and improved well-being."

For further information, refer to my own website https://handsforhealing.net

and the UK Reiki Federation website: https://reikifed.co.uk

Acupuncture

"Acupuncture is often used as a treatment for pain. This can be anything, including pain resulting from an injury, an acute pain, and chronic pain. Acupuncture can help with musculo-skeletal pain in joints or from arthritic conditions. It can also be used for all sorts of pain such as dental pain, headaches and migraines, through to digestive disorders such as IBS, resulting in stomach and intestinal pains. It can also treat pain from fibromyalgia. It is often used to treat lower back pain and neck and shoulder pain.

The theory of acupuncture is that it is based on lines of energy (meridians) which run through the body. Pain occurs where energy has become blocked and acupuncture works to release the block, thereby reducing or even banishing pain.

When choosing an acupuncturist, ensure that they are suitably qualified. They should be members of the British Acupuncture Council who are licensed by Environmental Health and have professional indemnity insurance, codes of ethics and confidentiality."

Lisa Collins, Proprietor and Practitioner

Lisa Collins Acupuncture

www.lisacollinsacupuncture.co.uk

Alexander Technique

"Our everyday actions and behaviours result in an accumulation of physical and mental strain. This builds up and causes illness, injuries and pains.

The Alexander Technique teaches how to identify which of our actions are causing us harm and how to re-establish natural balance and poise. This in turn can boost performance and bring relief to the pains and stresses caused by our postural habits.

It aims to promote an ease in our posture, helping our bodies to regain effective functions of the body and mind. This technique is useful throughout our whole lives."

Information sourced from The Society of Teachers of the Alexander Technique.

www.alexandertechnique.co.uk

Angelic Healing

"Angelic Healing is a form of energy which calls upon God and the angels to help you. During Angelic Healing, your aura and chakras will be cleansed and balanced, blockages removed. You need to have a sincere desire to be healed and to let go of all negativities, pain and painful emotions. You may still go through many trials, difficulties and life lessons."

Cathy Finch, Proprietor and Practitioner

Cathy Finch Angelic Healing

Email cathyfinch19@yahoo.co.uk

Aromatherapy

"Pain can take many forms in a person's life, so when choosing essential oils for pain management, it is important to be very clear about the following:

- the type of pain to be treated: acute, chronic, mental, emotional, or a combination of these.
- the chemical components within essential oils that will be the most helpful, e.g. pain with inflammation would benefit most from esters.
- the most appropriate oils containing those chemical components. For example, Roman chamomile and helichrysum are both high in esters. Thyme is high in phenols and peppermint contains a good proportion of the alcohol, menthol.

However, it is not enough just to select an effective blend of oils; careful thought must be given to the most effective way for the blend to be administered, e.g. massage, baths, compresses, vaporisers, etc.

Some essential oils that are commonly used to combat physical pain include: eucalyptus, clary sage, peppermint, thyme ct linalool, black pepper, Roman chamomile, lavender, marjoram, rosemary and ginger.

However, for emotional pain such as stress, anxiety and depression, the following oils are helpful: bergamot, clary sage, petitgrain, geranium, mandarin, melissa, neroli, patchouli, rose, ylang ylang, frankincense."

For more information, please visit www.ifaroma.org

International Federation of Aromatherapists.

Bach Flower Remedies

"Dr Bach said, 'Take no notice of the disease, think only of the outlook on life of the one in distress.' With this in mind in relation to pain, I still follow this guideline.

When we take a drop of remedy, our energetic field or aura receives the essence of the flower. Sounds fanciful. Energetic medicine is very real. These remedies put a positive energy into our energetic field and lift our systems so we can release negativity in the form of specific mental and emotional states.

It is our fears, cares, worries, anxieties, likes and dislikes that open the path to the invasion of illness. Works well and unobtrusively, you won't even think about it, with no side effects.

By alleviating negative feelings and relieving the underlying emotional and psychological problems, a physical healing is enabled and pain relieved."

Shirley Manning

Proprietor and Practitioner

Reiki-By-Shirley

www.reiki-by-shirley.com

shirley.reiki.master@gmail.com

Chakrascension™ and Pain Relief Chakrascension

"Chakrascension™ and Pain Relief Chakrascension use Ascended Master energy to balance and activate the main chakras in the human energy field. Each chakra is aligned to a specific area of the human physical body and to specific areas of the human condition. For example, the base chakra located at the base of the spine is linked on a physical level to the lower limbs, small intestine and colon. Therefore, energising this chakra can help healing and the alleviation in the related physical areas. This chakra is also associated with issues of security and survival. Imbalance in this chakra can cause feelings of insecurity and stress. Conditions which can be caused by stress, such as fibromyalgia, can be helped by using Chakrascension™ to release the energy blockages within the chakras. This can help with pain relief and accelerate healing. As the Chakras align with the endocrine system, Chakrascension™ can also be used to stimulate these which can release pain controlling hormones."

Alan Harris, co-creator, Practitioner and Instructor

Chakrascension ™

Website: www.chakrascension.org.uk

Counselling

"One in four of us are likely to experience a mental or emotional well-being issue at some point in our lives. There is usually a reason for the emotional pain this causes.

Seeking the help of a professional counsellor can help you to elucidate, work through and find potential solutions to the problems which cause you emotional turmoil in a totally confidential setting.

There are many different types of counselling available and the British Association of Counselling and Psychotherapy website (www.bacp.co.uk) provides a great deal of valuable information to enable you to find the most appropriate help for you."

Dot Wilson.

Cranial sacral therapy

"Cranial sacral therapy is a gentle touch therapy which facilitates an energetic unwinding of an individual's unique layers of physical and emotional imbalance which have occurred over time, through life events and shocks.

The aim of the treatment is to unwind areas of tension and stagnation which can prevent a healthy flow of energy and blood flow around the body. Energy cannot flow through a vacuum or an area that is blocked. If you are too tight, energy is sent to that area to unwind them and areas that are too loose will be wound up and tightened.

This helps to bring resilience into the body, which enables the client to withstand life's 'knocks'."

Caroline Frost, Proprietor and Practitioner

Caroline's Body Balance

Find me on Facebook:

https://www.facebook.com/carolinesbodybalance

Crystal Healing

"I am a Reiki Master Teacher Energy Healing Practitioner. I also incorporate crystals into the healing process.

I have something called a crystal pyramid, which has a different sound to that of a singing bowl or gong. It is a very gentle sound and it helps me to attune with the person receiving healing. Not only are you surrounded by the crystals but you are also immersed in sounds.

It has helped me to hear the change of tone in someone's auric field when it has something I may like to work with later, and guides me to where there may be an energy block within someone. Once I have tuned into your body's requirements at that time, I will then also be guided to use a variety or just one other crystal that may assist in the rebalance and detoxification that may be required by the body or systems.

I have been practising energy healing in one form or another for over thirty years and was also a registered spiritual healer in churches before Reiki became another of my life path journeys."

Judy Fenton

Proprietor and Practitioner.

Guided Hands Energy Healing.

Facebook Page: www.facebook.com/Guided-Hands-Energy-Healing-246182029388214/

Email address: fentonjudy@ymail.com

Cupping

"Cupping therapy places heated glass (or plastic with vents on) cups on the skin to create a vacuum. By doing this, the cups act like a reverse massage, lifting the top few centimetres of tissue into the cup. This relaxes muscles and increases blood flow, lymph drainage and aids removal of toxins, which can build up in stagnant areas where muscles are tight.

The treatment can be conducted in two ways: a rapid; tonifying way, which is unlikely to leave a mark, unless there was an excess of old blood that has leached out into the tissue. When conducted in this way, a 'popping' action of the cups being released quickly can send a vibration deep into the tissue. This can help break down areas of stagnation, both physical and energetic. The other method involves leaving the cups in place to increase blood flow to a specific area and the length of time denotes how much of a mark that can be left.

Clients may experience a deep coloured mark, which will just be old blood lifted to the surface. Only if cups are left for extended periods can capillary blood be leached to the surface. But even then, the resulting 'bruise' shouldn't be too painful as its not resulting from trauma."

Caroline Frost, Proprietor and Practitioner

Caroline's Body Balance

Find me on Facebook:

https://www.facebook.com/carolinesbodybalance

Emmett Technique

"The EMMETT Technique is a unique form of body relaxation therapy for both people and animals, involving the application of light finger pressure at specific points. It is based on the belief that light touch can trigger a relaxation response in the soft tissues of the body, and that the therapist may thereby help relieve feelings of tension.

Many people find they feel more at ease within their body and their emotional well-being is enhanced. Animals appear calmer and at ease. The result is often an instantaneous feeling of greater comfort.

The EMMETT Technique is truly a complementary therapy. It may be applied in isolation but it also combines easily with all other bodywork and exercise specialities such as massage, chiropractic, physiotherapy, Bowen therapy, craniosacral therapy, yoga, Pilates and personal training as some typical examples.

Visit www.emmett-uk.co.uk for more information and to read testimonials from clients and practitioners." EMMETT Therapies UK.

Emotional Freedom Technique (E.F.T.)

"Emotional Freedom Technique (EFT) is simply described as psychological acupuncture without needles. The treatment involves tapping meridian points on the face and body, which can help restore the body back to balance. How this works is that a subject will rate the intensity level of the issue/pain/emotion from 1-10, with 10 being highest, and as they tap the points the intensity level will reduce in most cases.

This technique can help with pain, trauma, anxiety, fears, weight issues and almost anything with an emotional charge."

Sonya Rigby, Proprietor and Practitioner

Sonya Holistic Therapies

Facebook page: www.facebook.com/Sonya-Holistic-Therapies-426318251051503/

Hypnotherapy

"Unnecessary Suffering - When it comes to pain, a certain amount is there to keep us safe, and let us know we need to pay attention to certain elements of your physical, emotional and spiritual well-being.

However, as human beings we tend to hang on to, amplify and even identify ourselves with that pain. This pain is useless and is kept alive by our unconscious minds, often well after the original hurt has gone. Thoughts shape your reality. If your unconscious mind is holding on to that pain ,you are suffering unnecessarily.

Through hypnosis, you will discover new ways to experience

life without all the unnecessary pain. I want you to just imagine how that can feel when we work together as you start to notice the possibilities as well as freedom that being free of unnecessary pain will bring."

Rob Chapman

Proprietor and Practitioner

IMeditate

www.robchapman.org.uk

Kinesiology

"The therapy uses muscle monitoring to discover what might be causing stresses and imbalances in a person's energy system. As the focus of kinesiology is on supporting the person's energy system, there are many areas of an individual's health and life that could benefit from kinesiology.

People have found that kinesiology has helped them with:

· Overcoming past trauma

· Identifying nutritional excess or deficiency and allergies

· Eliminating emotional, physical and mental stress

· Releasing fears and phobias

· Assisting with decision-making

· Improving sports performance

· Enhancing learning abilities

· Aiding in muscle injury healing

During a kinesiology session, the client remains fully clothed. The kinesiologist will move the client's arm or leg into a specific position, so the muscle is contracted. Light pressure is then applied against the muscle that is being tested while the client is asked to match the pressure.

This is not a test of the strength of the muscle but of how the muscle responds to the stimulus of the added pressure. The muscle will either remain in contraction or will unlock. How the muscle responds gives the kinesiologist bio-feedback and this is used to determine what the priority stresses are and how best to address them. At no time should the client experience pain or discomfort with the testing."

Bettina Katz

Representative, The Kinesiology Federation.

For more information visit: www.kinesiologyfederation.co.uk

Massage

'When you bang your arm, or head, etc, you rub it - this is the basis of massage! On a physical level, this causes an increase in the blood and lymph circulation, soft tissue is able to respond positively to the increase in oxygen and essential nutrients delivered in the blood and there is a reduction in the pain/discomfort initially experienced. Massage has a calming, relaxing effect, allowing the client to reduce their stress levels and anxiety, alongside the positive effect on long-term illness symptoms such as cramps, digestive issues, insomnia, etc. The versatility of massage makes it an effective treatment for nearly every person in one format or another to bring pain reduction, improved mobility, peacefulness and calm, to name but a few."

National Association of Massage and Manipulative Therapists

Website: www.nammt.co.uk

McLoughlin Scar Tissue Release – MSTR

"MSTR is a brilliant soft tissue technique that can help deepen and complete the healing process for almost any scar tissue including burn scars, regardless of its location or age. As all scar tissue, whether by accident or surgery, represents a trauma for the body, the healing can often be incomplete. This may present as red, sore, itchy, puckered and hypersensitive scars. It can also lead to loss of sensation, numbness, pain in local or seemingly unrelated places (appendix scars commonly see issue present in left shoulder). The technique is very client led, relatively painless, and permanent. It can significantly improve all of the aforementioned symptoms and can even dramatically change the appearance and visibility of scars (although this is not the primary purpose of the treatment). As long as a scar is fully healed, it can generally be worked with. It may require several sessions to gain the full benefits, but changes can be seen and felt almost immediately. It can also help the body to process any stored emotional residue from the scar trauma as well as restore the flow of Qi in any of the acupuncture meridians affected by the scar."

Ben Calder, Practitioner

Centre For Integral Health

Website: https://bencalder.co.uk/

MSTR: https://bencalder.co.uk/services/mcloughlin-scar tissue-release-mstr/

My governing body: Association of Physical and Natural Therapists: https://apnt.org/

BCMA: https://bcma.co.uk/

Meditation

"Mindfulness and meditation are the same and both involve observing what is happening in the body by carrying out an internal body scan. By sitting quietly, closing your eyes and working up from the feet to the head inch by inch, you will examine every part of the body and notice, without judgement, where the pain is. Pain causes tension to the body. Therefore, when we stop and become mindful of the body and where we perceive the pain to be and examine this pain internally, you can then learn gentle breathing exercises that will help reduce the tension which, in turn, can help reduce the pain. You will also learn about distractions that can help you when your pain is high, such as playing a game on your iPad, reading, or talking to friends."

June Meagher

Proprietor and Instructor

AAMAR Healing

www.amaarhealing.co.uk and

www.junemeagher.com

Naturopathy

"Naturopaths are akin to general practitioners and have a range of therapeutic tools at their disposal.

Pain is a subjective symptom, and it important for a naturopath to take a full and detailed case history to identify the origin and causes of pain – be it physical, spiritual, mental or emotional.

Naturopathy has as its basic tenet 'the healing power of nature', and physical pain, depending upon its origin, could be treated to encourage balance/equilibrium with structural correction (many naturopaths are also osteopaths) or kinesiology, with herbs, with hydrotherapy (thermotherapy), or massage.

Naturopaths are also trained in psychosocial techniques and can address pain through counselling, homeopathy, lifestyle modification, or refer on to a specialist. Depending upon their chosen speciality, naturopathic herbalists will use herbs homeopaths their remedies and so on."

General Naturopathic Council

RG19082019

https://gncouncil.co.uk

Neuro Linguistic Programming – NLP

"NLP can help pinpoint the where/why/when of an underlying thought pattern or behaviour. The therapist helps the client to relax into a meditative state, which enables a direct link to the subconscious to be established. By talking with the sub-conscious, the client need not be fully aware of the reasons behind their discomfort.

One of the main benefits of NLP is that the client doesn't need to explain their issue in any great detail to the therapist, or at all, if it is upsetting for them to discuss consciously. The therapist can ask simple, non-leading questions to elicit enough information, to guide the client to do the work needed to disrupt the negative neural pathways. The disruption changes the emotional response associated with the state, helping to make it harder to recall after the session is over.

The techniques can be so successful that minimal sessions are needed to make a lasting change."

Caroline Frost,Proprietor and Practitioner

Caroline's Body Balance

Facebook page: www.facebook.com/carolinesbodybalance

Pilates

"The Pilates Method was developed by German-born Joseph Pilates (1883-1967), who originally designed his exercise method, Contrology, for army and police cadets, but ended up in New York, where his main clientele were dancers. Pilates is both mind- and body-conditioning. It can be practised in a studio with specialist equipment or as mat work, in 1:1 sessions, or group classes. It should be noted that there are many different schools and styles of Pilates, some are physically more limited than others and may not be as suitable for anyone suffering with pain.

Body Control Pilates has a unique, safe and well-respected approach. Clients learn the Fundamentals of Alignment (awareness of good posture), Breathing (very useful for relaxation and pain management), and Centring (or core stability, which is very beneficial for the management of back, pelvic and hip pain). With regular practice, your joints become more mobile, appropriately supported by surrounding muscles. Your spine becomes more flexible, your back strong.

Above all, Pilates improves your body awareness and puts you back in control of your body. It gives you the confidence to become more active. All exercises are performed mindfully, in a supportive, non-competitive, environment. Whilst generic Pilates may be helpful for reducing pain, it is worth hunting out experienced teachers who have further training in topics such as back pain (see below). Find a small class (no more than 12 participants), where the teacher asks about your health beforehand and then adapts the exercises accordingly. Avoid large classes where everyone does the same exercises.'

Body Control Pilates UK

For a local Body Control Pilates teacher, visit:

www.bodycontrolpilates.com

Look on this website for Back4Good® and Healthy backs practitioners.

For a link to research Pilates, please visit:

www.pilates.com/pilates/library/bibliography

Psychics, Mediums and Clairvoyants

"As a psychic medium, I regularly meet people who have deep-seated pain that they have buried, believing that it no longer affects them. During a reading, I can be shown issues people have had in their lifetime. The majority of people hold on to negativity and may change based on that experience. They think they have dealt with it... which they haven't.

I have taught myself over the years why people hold certain energies in different parts of the body. One of things my Guide said to me as I was walking through a supermarket was, 'Would you let everyone put their shopping in your trolley and pay for it?' I replied 'No.' 'So,' he said, 'why do humans allow others to put their issues and problems within their soul? You get filled with other energies and then life becomes heavier and heavier to a point where it can make you ill – emotionally, mentally or physically.'

I realised the biggest thing that helps is forgiving those who have caused us pain, including ourselves. I find that when I pick up aches, pains or emotional issues during a reading, it makes them sit up and readdress their life, more so as I don't know these people. Grief is one thing we all have to experience and one which affects us all in different ways. Grief is personal to yourself. You have different memories and regrets. Learning to grieve is so important, otherwise it can make you ill.

One thing I find that helps is connecting to the inner you using meditation. Being in the moment helps you to find the inner you. It is about the intention when meditating. What is your purpose? – to relax, go into different realms, to look at your future pathways and so much more. Often people say, 'I cannot meditate.' I suggest they learn breathing techniques... then start with a ten-minute meditation. There are plenty on YouTube. Having the right type of music and the sound of a person's voice is the key. Get comfortable and warm... Your mind will wander the first few times but you will find it easier the more you do it. Meditation can help with stress, pain and anxiety."

Jane Lightfoot, Proprietor, Practitioner and Instructor. Mystique Psychic and Wellbeing Centre.

https://www.facebook.com/Mystique-1279041398876834

https://www.mystiquewellbeing4.me/

Qigong

'Qigong (pronounced 'chee gong') is an ancient exercise discipline from China and has over 3500 different forms including Tai Chi, the most recognised form. Qigong is a mindful movement practice that co-ordinates breathing and graceful, gentle movements and standing practices. The practices assist in the unlinking of residual tensions in the body, re-aligning poor posture, re-linking movement into healthy, energy generating movements and building strength. The aim is to develop a smooth and even flow of Qi (vital lifeforce energy) to allow for optimal physical, emotional and energetic function for the body and mind. The practice is suitable for all ages and abilities. It's made so easy by the 'less than 70% rule' we employ, to train people to recognise their own edge of capability and to always practise below this edge, activating but not exhausting the body."

Ben Calder, Instructor

Centre For Integral Health.

My website www.bencalder.co.uk/

Qigong www.bencalder.co.uk/services/qigong-for-health/

My governing body – Association of Physical and Natural Therapists www.apnt.org/

BCMA: www.bcma.co.uk/

Reflexology

"Reflexology is an ancient treatment that works on meridians on the feet that correlate to the parts of the body. As the points on the feet are worked on, the body goes into relaxation, thus helping the body reach a state of balance so that healing can take place.

This can help clear energy and blockages in the area of disease or illness, can help relax and lift the mood then in this state pain is felt less. It can also boost the immune system."

Sonya Rigby, Proprietor and Practitioner

Sonya Holistic Therapies

Shamanic Healing

"Shamanic healing is ancient, it's the process of restoring mental, physical, and spiritual balance.

It allows our bodies to clear what no longer serves purpose to us. In shamanic belief, this is stuck crystallised energy which has formed, over many years or even lifetimes. This can be removed releasing the body, allowing the chakra system to rid itself of 'Hootcha' and enabling the immune system to work as it should.

As a shamanic healer, I am a mesa carrier. I carry medicine stones in my mesa (portable altar), which are used as part of the healing. The sacred directions are opened, the individual lies down, my Wirococha (energy field) is opened and passed over myself and my client for protection. I will then check my client for blockages using my pendulum. The medicine stone is then placed on the blocked chakra. I will hold the client's head for some time while Hootcha (a black sludge which stops the chakras functioning fully) is released to Pachamamma.(Mother Earth)

While this is taking place, you are used as a vessel, allowing spirit to move through you. I will then track over the body and remove crystallised energy, using my hands, smudge stick and the rattle.

Once completed, love and light is passed back into the affected chakra and is sealed. The removal of Wirochocha completes the session.

The medicine allows the individual to once again step into their power, confidently, with free movement mentally and physically.

I studied the teachings of the Q'ero tribe from Peru."

Vicky Brown.

Find me on Facebook: https://www.facebook.com/West-Winds-Daughter-Shamanic-Healing-108067720698330.

Shiatsu

"Shiatsu can help alleviate pain on many levels. Physically much pain is caused by muscle tension, which in turn restricts joints and can refer pain via the nervous system. The sustained holding pressure used in Shiatsu has the effect of re-setting the nerves within muscles, increasing blood and lymph circulation and moving lactic acid, which may be causing cramps or spasms.

Emotional discomfort, anxiety, stress often stem from overactivity of our Autonomic Nervous System (the fight or flight mechanism). Shiatsu treatment often focuses on pressure points close to the spine, particularly at the neck and sacrum which have been found to calm the ANS and promote feelings of wellbeing. In addition, Shiatsu has been used traditionally to normalise hormonal activity and it is well known that our hormones regulate emotions: Seasonally Affected Disorder, Pre-Menstrual Syndrome and thyroid issues all affect our mood. Shiatsu Theory has explanations for these conditions which may include understanding of the meridians, acupoints and energy balance.

Sensitive, supportive touch can do much to alleviate distress for the elderly, the terminally ill and the lonely."

Elaine Liechti, Director, Shiatsu Society UK

To find recognised and insured Shiatsu practitioners please contact www.shiatsusociety.org

Sound Healing

"Sound Healing uses aspects of sound to bring about harmony to the mind, body and spirit. Whether you use the voice, sound healing instruments such as singing bowls, tuning forks or gongs, frequencies or music the intention is to make a person feel well and be 'in tune' with themselves.

Not only do you look at the person but also their environment, to ensure there are no conflicting sounds that can drain your health such as some electronic devices or external sounds like those omitted from pylons.

We are vibratory organisms and need to be in harmony in our surroundings and relationships including the one we have with ourselves."

June Meagher, Proprietor, Practitioner and Instructor

AAMAR Healing

For further information on June Meagher, visit:

www.aamarhealing.co.uk and www.junemeagher.com.

For further information on Sound Healing, visit:

www.collegeofsoundhealing.co.uk.

Spiritual Healing

"Spiritual Healing is a vast, sometimes complex, area of alternative therapy. It can help in so many ways, from Reiki to sound therapy. It can get to the core of the pain and where or what causes it. Are we holding on to things that do not serve us, yet we still hold onto them?

Pain comes in many forms from old wounds, or maybe

arthritis. The list goes on but over the years, in fact thousands of years, alternative therapies have been used to treat many illnesses and diseases.

The Native American Shamans used a vast knowledge of Spiritual Healing from sound to deep forms of meditation handed down from their ancestors. The aboriginal people of Australia were using the didgeridoo at least 1500 years ago as a healing tool.

As we are made up of energy, we can pick up a vibration or an energy that does not work well with our natural rhythm. This is where Spiritual Healing can work wonders in recalibrating the vibration that works best for us."

Kristian Ellis,Proprietor and Practitioner

Spiritual Healing with Kris.

Email: spiritualhealingkris@gmail.com

Yoga

"Yoga postures or 'Asanas' essentially refer to a state of being physically and mentally at ease, steady, quiet and comfortable. Regular practice of Asana maintains the physical body in an optimum condition, promoting health even in unhealthy bodies. Pain arises from dis-ease, essentially a lack of ease. Static asanas gently massage the internal organs, glands and muscles and relax the nerves of the body. Dynamic asanas increase flexibility, speed circulation, loosen the muscles and joints and release blocks in our Chi/energy flow. They tone the muscles, skin, encourage intestinal peristalsis and improve digestive health and transit.

Yoga is based in excellence and fulfilling oneself in the experience of being human. Fundamentally, yoga is health orientated and states 'Good health is your birthright!' Although it is not inherently a therapeutic model it has huge well-documented therapeutic benefits. A trained yoga teacher can help you select certain postures and sets to help alleviate your pain and discomfort."

Thomas Stacey is a BWY qualified Hatha Yoga instructor and also runs Kundalini Yoga , Tai chi Qigong and Gong bath 'Yoga of Sound' healing sessions, both publicly and privately.

His Facebook page is Shropshire Yoga.

His sound healing website is www.sacredsound.guru

Thomas Stacey, Practitioner and Instructor

Shropshire Yoga

Email Thomas at tomshanti909@outlook.com   for more details.

Printed in Great Britain
by Amazon